SURFACE
TENSION

SURFACE TENSION

To all the men, women
and children lost at sea,
in body or soul.

Dedicated to Rosa.

ISBN: 9781785855139

MARCH 2016. FIRST PRINTING.

Published by Titan Comics, a division of Titan
Publishing Group, Ltd. 144 Southwark Street,
London SE1 0UP. Originally published in single
comic form as *Surface Tension #1-5*. *Surface
Tension* is trademark™ and copyright © 2015 Jay
Gunn. All rights reserved.

Printed in China. TC1815.

A CIP catalogue record for this title is available
from the British Library.

WWW.TITAN-COMICS.COM

@COMICSTITAN

 FACEBOOK.COM/COMICSTITAN

Lettered by
Comicraft's Jimmy Betancourt
& Albert Deschesne

Editor
Andrew James

Assistant Editor Emeritus
Kirsten Murray

Collection Designer
Rob Farmer

TITAN COMICS

SENIOR EDITOR
Steve White

EDITORIAL
Lizzie Kaye, Tom Williams

PRODUCTION MANAGER
Jackie Flook, Maria Pearson

PRODUCTION ASSISTANT
Peter James

STUDIO MANAGER
Selina Juneja

SENIOR SALES MANAGER
Steve Tothill

SENIOR MARKETING & PRESS OFFICER
Owen Johnson

**DIRECT SALES AND
MARKETING MANAGER**
Ricky Claydon

COMMERCIAL MANAGER
Michelle Fairlamb

PUBLISHING MANAGER
Darryl Tothill

PUBLISHING DIRECTOR
Chris Teather

OPERATIONS DIRECTOR
Leigh Baulch

EXECUTIVE DIRECTOR
Vivian Cheung

PUBLISHER
Nick Landau

SURFACE TENSION

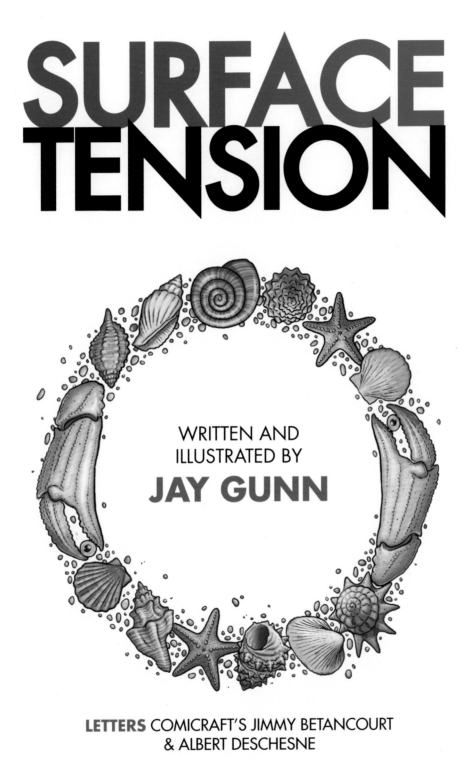

WRITTEN AND
ILLUSTRATED BY

JAY GUNN

LETTERS COMICRAFT'S JIMMY BETANCOURT
& ALBERT DESCHESNE

TITAN
COMICS

www.titan-comics.com

HRRRMF!

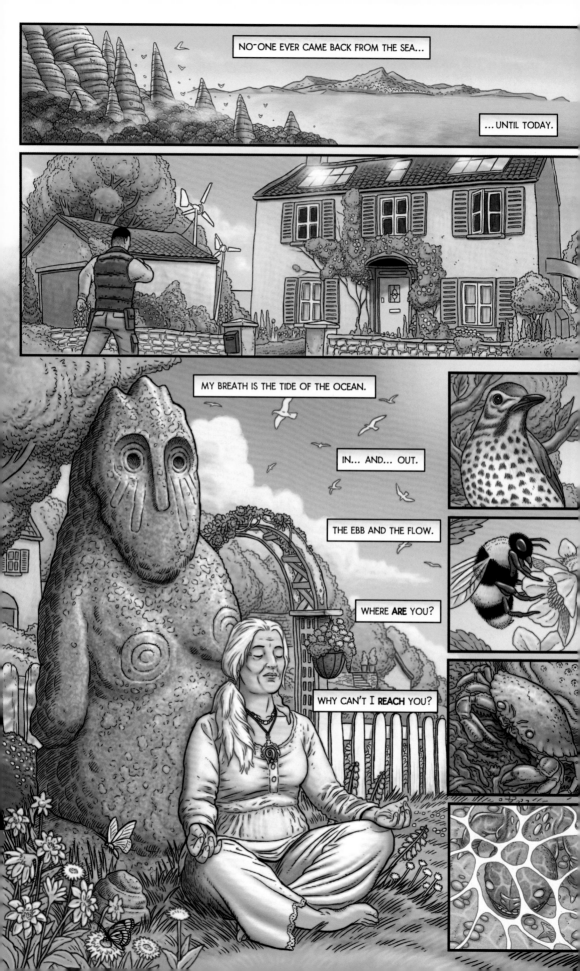

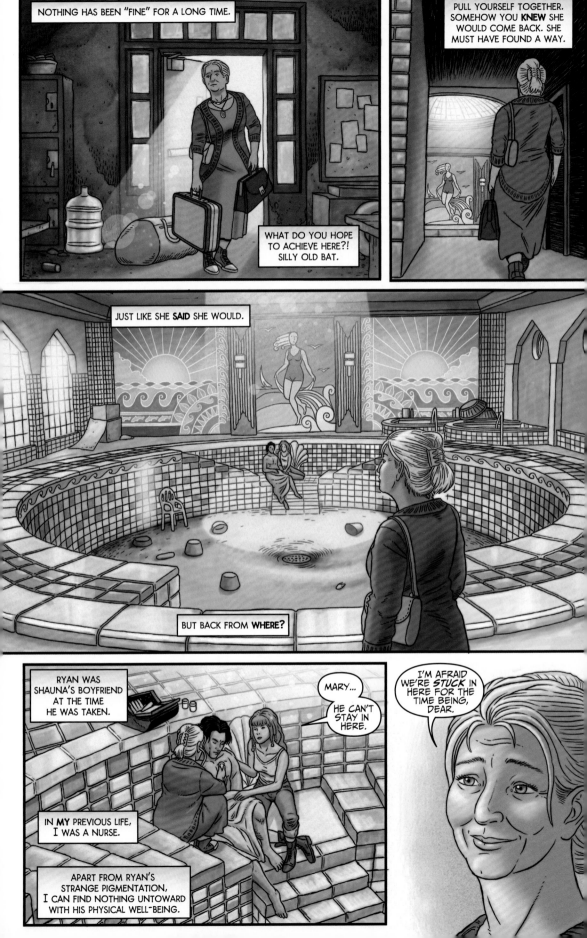

CAN YOU TELL WHAT'S *WRONG* WITH US?

THAT'S WHAT I'M HERE TO FIND OUT. BUT I'M GOING TO NEED YOUR *HELP.*

DID HE TELL YOU ANYTHING ABOUT HIS EXPERIENCES? WHERE HE'S *BEEN* ALL THIS TIME?

NO... HE REMEMBERS NOTHING.

BUT... HE'S STILL *RYAN.* HE'S STILL THE MAN I KNEW.

IT'S GOOD THAT YOU'RE HERE FOR HIM, SHAUNA. HE'S GOING TO NEED YOU.

WHAT ABOUT THE OTHER ONE? MEGUMI?

SHE'S IN THE SHOWER ROOM. SHE WOULDN'T LET ME HELP HER.

MEG -- MEGUMI?

IT'S ME -- MARY. I CAME, JUST AS YOU ASKED.

M...MARY...

OH, MARY!

POOR DARLING! HUSH, NOW. YOU'RE SAFE.

I WAS SO SCARED. WHAT'S *HAPPENING* TO ME?

THE CORAL SENTINELS CONTINUED TO GROW AND TO SPREAD. THEN THE CREATURES CAME.

NEW FORMS OF LIFE SPRANG FROM THE SEA.

MOST WERE HARMLESS... BUT NOT **ALL**.

THE BIGGEST AMONG THEM ATTACK ANY ATTEMPT TO SET SAIL. WE'RE CUT OFF, NOW, FROM THE REST OF THE WORLD.

AN ISLAND IN THE TRUEST SENSE OF THE WORD.

WHAT ABOUT MY *FAMILY* -- MY LITTLE BROTHER, KYLE?

THIS CAN'T... IT CAN'T BE *HAPPENING*!

IT **HAS** HAPPENED. PAST TENSE.

WE CAME TO TERMS WITH **OUR** LOSSES LONG AGO.

THEY'RE ONLY JUST LEARNING OF THEIRS. AN ACHING REMINDER OF WHAT WE ALL WENT THROUGH.

YOU DON'T REMEMBER COMING TO SEE ME?

NO... I -- I FEEL LIKE SOMEONE'S BEEN CUTTING OUT PIECES OF MY *BRAIN*.

...AND YOUR DISCOVERY IN *GHANA?* YOU AND *ERIK?*

GHANA...

YES! *THAT* I REMEMBER!

ERIK... HE *FOUND* IT!

DID... DID HE *CAUSE* ALL OF THIS...?

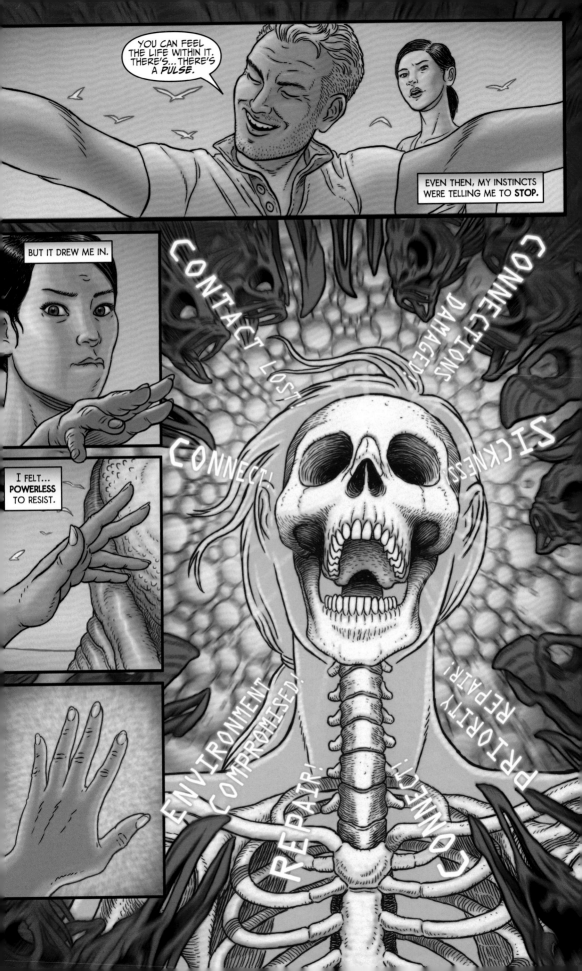

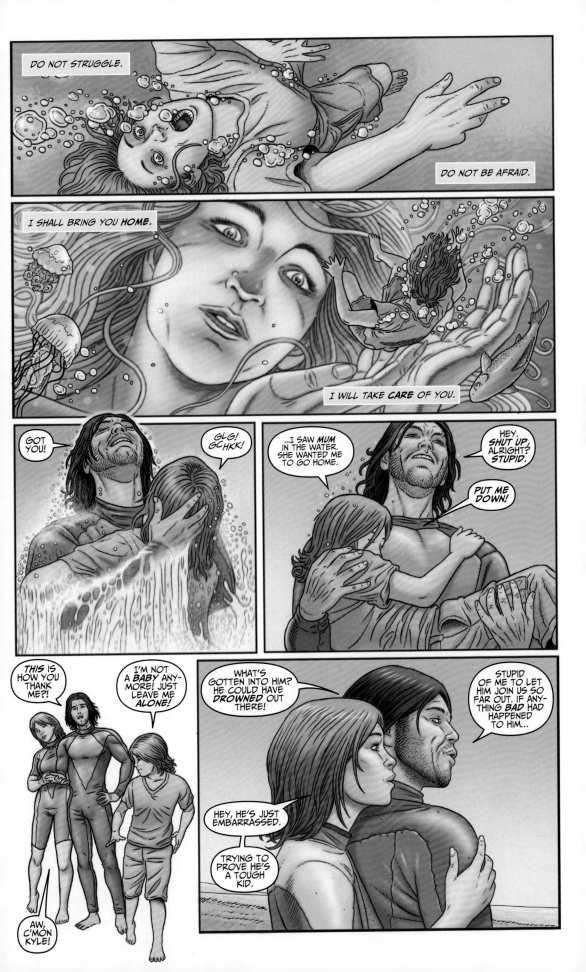

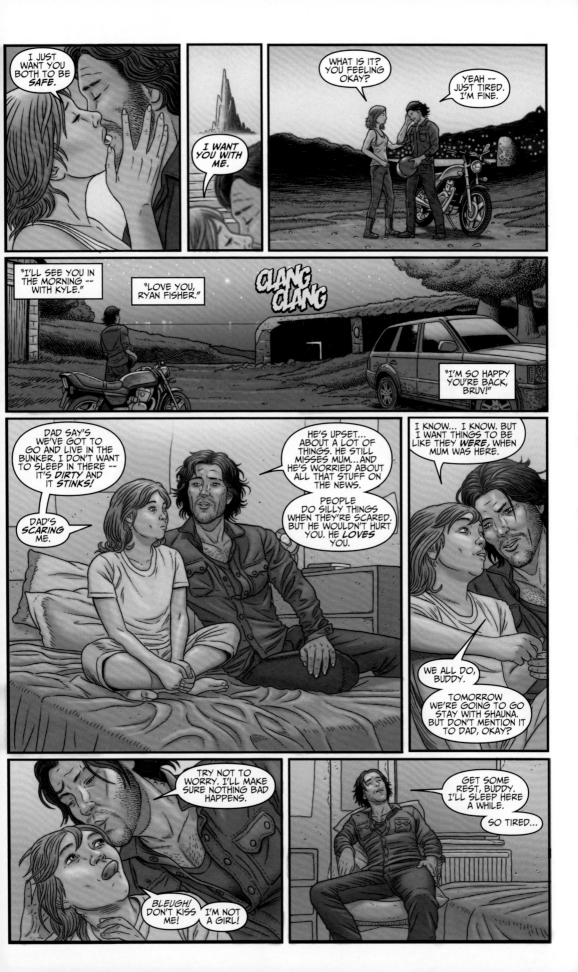

"AFTER ERIK DISAPPEARED, YOU WROTE TO ME. I WAS TERRIBLY WORRIED ABOUT WHAT HAD HAPPENED IN GHANA.

"IT ALWAYS FELT LIKE I WAS COMING *HOME* WHEN I CAME TO VISIT BREITH.

"GEOF AND I PERSUADED YOU TO COME AND STAY WITH US HERE ON BREITH."

"YES. YES, I REMEMBER NOW!

MEG, YOU POOR DARLING!

"BUT EVEN HERE, THERE WAS NO ESCAPE.

THEY APPEARED A MONTH AGO. AT FIRST THEY WERE QUITE THE ATTRACTION.

NOW I UNDERSTAND THEY'RE POPPING UP ALL OVER THE WORLD.

YES.

...AND THE PEOPLE DOWN THERE?

"WE CALL THEM THE *SHELL PEOPLE.* THEY IDOLIZE THE CORALS AS SOME SORT OF... SPIRITUAL TOTEM. THEY BELIEVE IT'S THEIR CALLING TO RETURN TO THE SEA -- THAT THE CORALS WILL TAKE THEM TO A *BETTER* WORLD.

"THEIR NUMBERS ARE *GROWING,* BUT THEY SEEM HARMLESS ENOUGH.

"DESPITE THE HORRORS OF GHANA AND THE SHADOW OF THE SENTINELS ACROSS THE WORLD, I FELT AT LAST, FOR THE FIRST TIME IN MONTHS -- A MOMENT OF PEACE.

"I DON'T KNOW IF I EVER *THANKED* YOU OR GEOF FOR YOUR KINDNESS."

IT FEELS LIKE HE'S TRYING TO *CONTACT* ME.

I SAW HIM *DIE*, MARY. IT *TOOK* HIM AND I'M TO BLAME.

GEOF, BE A DARLING AND PUT THE *KETTLE* ON, LOVE.

MEDITATION GURU

SCIENCE NOW

GEOF MAYBEL WINS ECOLOGY AWARD!

FUKUSHIMA'S ATOMIC LEGACY

BEFORE WE FOUND THE CORAL... MY RELATIONSHOP WITH ERIK WAS FALLING APART.

I FELT THAT ALL OUR WORK WAS FOR NOTHING BUT *VANITY*. I STOPPED *BELIEVING*.

NO-ONE COULD SAVE THE PLANET. IT WAS BETTER OFF WITHOUT US.

I WAS... *EMPTY* INSIDE. I PUSHED ERIK AWAY.

THAT'S WHEN HE FOUND IT. THE FIRST CORAL.

"ERIK WANTED SO BADLY FOR ME TO BELIEVE IN HIM. I THINK HE DID WHAT HE DID... FOR *ME*.

"TO PROVE A *POINT*."

YOU MUSTN'T BLAME YOURSELF. IF IT HADN'T BEEN ERIK, IT WOULD HAVE TAKEN SOMEONE ELSE.

WE DON'T UNDERSTAND WHAT SORT OF *HOLD* THOSE THINGS HAVE OVER THE HUMAN MIND.

"...IN MY DREAMS... I SEE A MASKED FIGURE ON A BEACH.

"EPHEMERAL."

"IT TURNS TO THE SEA, AND I HEAR THE SAME WORD EVERY TIME...

"SOON."

"THEN I WAKE."

MARY, I NEED TO UNDERSTAND WHAT THIS MEANS.

I NEED YOU TO PERFORM *HYPNOSIS* ON ME.

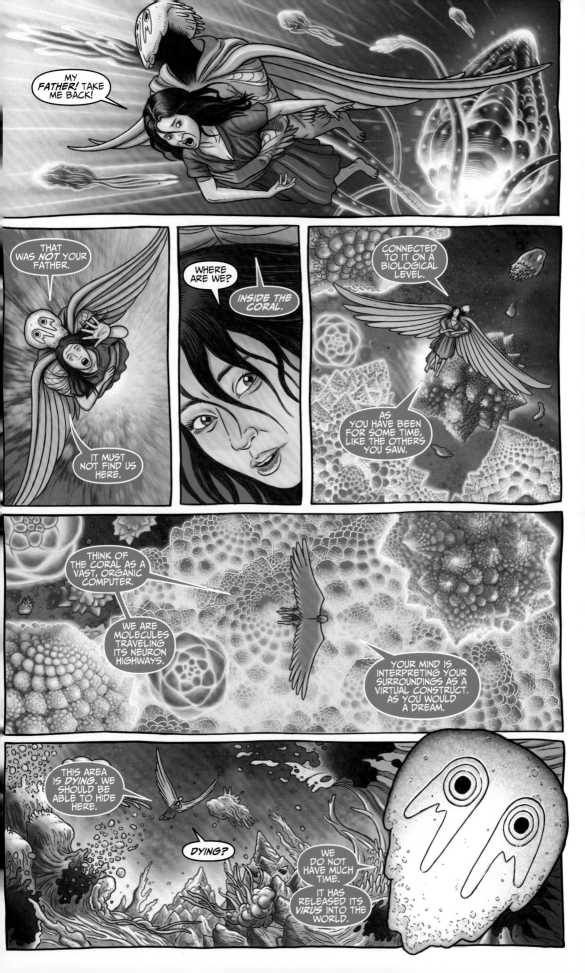

BLAM

BLAM

BLAM

NOW THAT I HAVE YOUR *ATTENTION*--

JEAN?

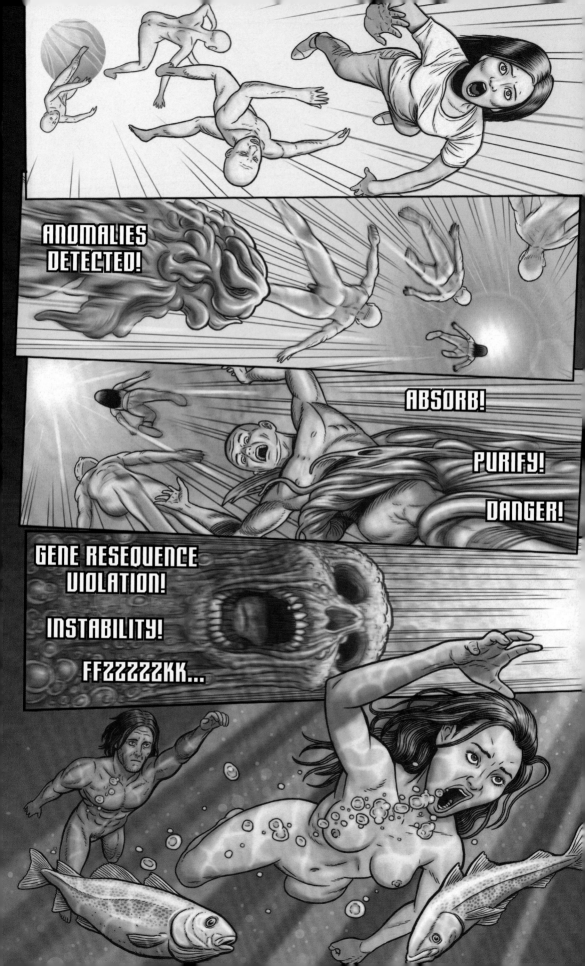

"WHEN YOUR KIND RETURN, *WE* WILL BE WAITING."

MEG?

IT'S. OVER. THE CORALS ARE BREAKING UP. THEIR HUSKS WILL NOURISH THE SEAS...

AND YOU, IN THEIR TURN.

IT'S... BEAUTIFUL!

YOU... DID IT, MEGUMI! YOU SAVED US.

HMMMM... I HOPE THAT I DO NOT *REGRET* THAT DECISION.

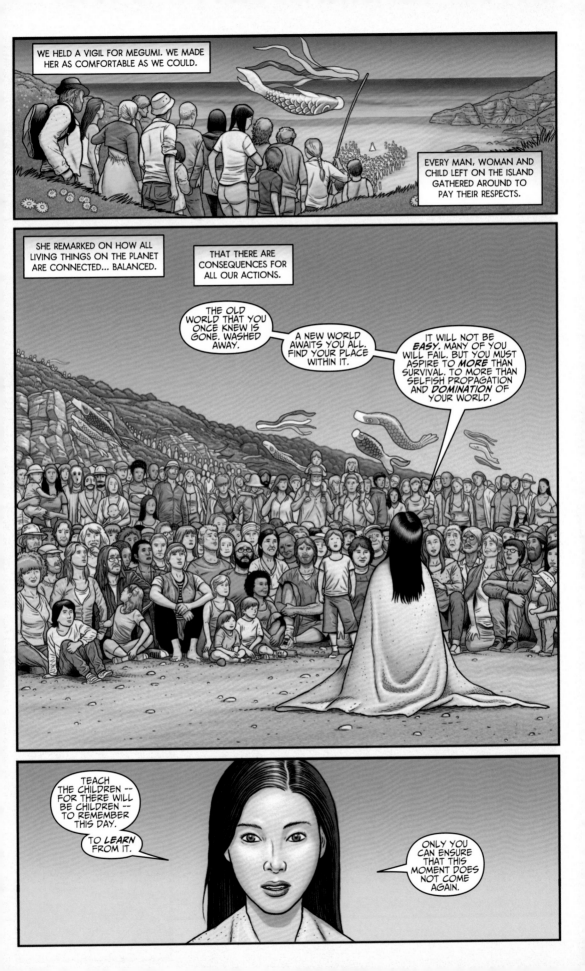

WE HELD A VIGIL FOR MEGUMI. WE MADE HER AS COMFORTABLE AS WE COULD.

EVERY MAN, WOMAN AND CHILD LEFT ON THE ISLAND GATHERED AROUND TO PAY THEIR RESPECTS.

SHE REMARKED ON HOW ALL LIVING THINGS ON THE PLANET ARE CONNECTED... BALANCED.

THAT THERE ARE CONSEQUENCES FOR ALL OUR ACTIONS.

THE OLD WORLD THAT YOU ONCE KNEW IS GONE. WASHED AWAY.

A NEW WORLD AWAITS YOU ALL. FIND YOUR PLACE WITHIN IT.

IT WILL NOT BE *EASY.* MANY OF YOU WILL FAIL. BUT YOU MUST ASPIRE TO *MORE* THAN SURVIVAL. TO MORE THAN SELFISH PROPAGATION AND *DOMINATION* OF YOUR WORLD.

TEACH THE CHILDREN -- FOR THERE WILL BE CHILDREN -- TO REMEMBER THIS DAY.

TO *LEARN* FROM IT.

ONLY YOU CAN ENSURE THAT THIS MOMENT DOES NOT COME AGAIN.

MARY'S JOURNAL

With the corals gone, so too are the monstrous leviathans that circled our island. With their leaving comes newfound freedom – and once again, children are able to play in the sea. There is no fear in the sound of their laughter – this is their time now.

There is renewed talk and much excitement at the prospect of leaving the island, but also uncertainty at the unknown. One thing that *is* for certain, our place in this world is by no means assured. Our previous entitlement and arrogance, our belief that we are the masters of this world, has been replaced with fear, respect and humility. Do we spread out across the seas as future conquerors... or as protectors of this fragile planet?

And what of the selkie...? These strange, gentle marine creatures that observe us with keen, intelligent eyes. At once familiar and yet so alien. By mistake, or design, the selkie have evolved from the biological soup that was to have been the end of our species. With their evolution enhanced by the science of the corals, the selkie have adapted remarkably well to their new environment. It's quite possible that they are the *true* heirs of this new world.

My thoughts turn to the cosmic beings that built the corals. Undoubtedly a remarkably advanced civilization, had we been able to communicate with them, what wisdom could they have bestowed? Wiped out by our hand, without our even being aware of their presence on this Earth. How many *other*, terrestrial species have been lost due to human activity – with no mark of their passing? Perhaps the extinctions that ultimately resulted from our unchecked and untimely destruction were always going to prefigure our inevitable demise. If not by the sea-sickness, then some other unforeseen catastrophe. Everything is connected.

When and if they return to this world, will they do so as vengeful gods? Or will they look upon us with forgiveness?

...that is a story for another day.

FIVE MONTHS LATER.

THE END

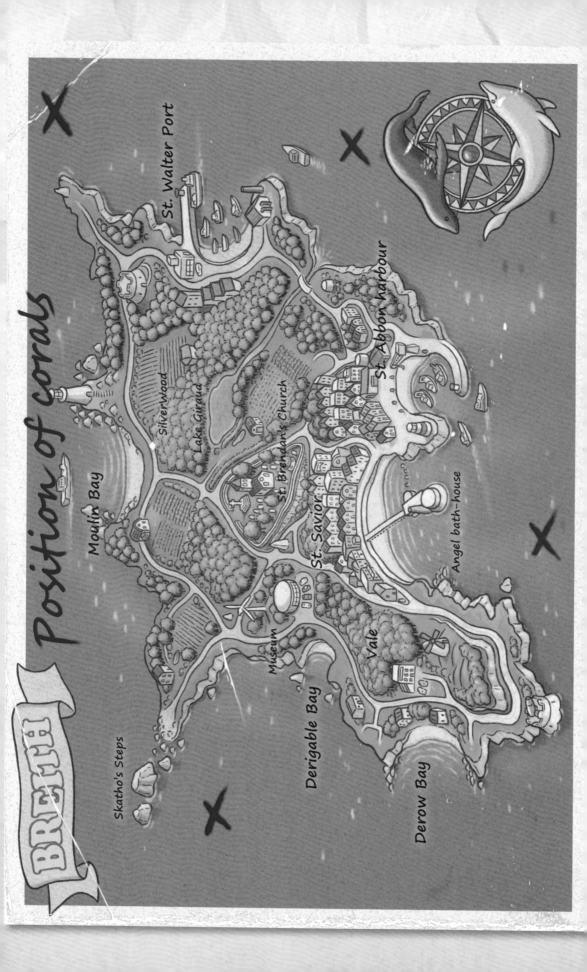